D1603941

Reach Around Books Season Two...

Who Will Help Jack Off the Horse?

Brenda's Beaver Plays a Round

JiggleWiggleTicklePickle

Lucy Lickalotopus Goes Down South

Peter Pitched a Tent

Reach Around Books Season One...

Suzy Likes to Look at Balls

Come Swing with Us!

Put Tony's Nuts in Your Mouth!

Spank the Monkey Lends a Hand

Brenda's Beaver Needs a Barber

www.ReachAroundBooks.com

JiggleWiggleTicklePickle

written by Bimisi Tayanita

illustrated by Sumguyen Bangladesh

created by Matt Williams, smuggler

ISBN 978-1-946178-09-1   First printing   Printed with love, in China.

"JiggleWiggleTicklePickle" is the third of five books that make up Season Two.

www.ReachAroundBooks.com

I've found many shapes and sizes
I've seen more than you'd guess

Sit down in that chair right there
and let me tell you who's the best

If you want to spend two months
                with an itchy rash

JiggleWiggleTicklePickle is not the one to ask

JiggleWiggleTicklePickle is clean and he is safe

He won't make you gag, I might add

...or squirt you in the face

JiggleWiggleTicklePickle knows your favorite spot

JiggleWiggleTicklePickle is ready when he's not

JiggleWiggleTicklePickle will slide right up inside

He'll wiggle and he'll jiggle
and he'll take you for a ride

Even if it takes an hour he's gonna get you there

...and if you haven't shaved or showered
he really doesn't care

He doesn't have a hairy back...
his feet have never stunk

JiggleWiggleTicklePickle doesn't come home drunk

He won't leave his seed on your favorite skirt
and make your sheets a mess

...or clean up with your new silk shirt
   like half the guys you've ever met

JiggleWiggleTicklePickle has nothing to unload

You can let him in and still be thin
nine months down the road

While most guys boast and lie
    about their floppy, little worm

JiggleWiggleTicklePickle is long and thick and firm

JiggleWiggleTicklePickle isn't loud or rude

He's super chill, and always will
   let you set the mood

Some days you play along the edge
...soft, and slow, and sweet

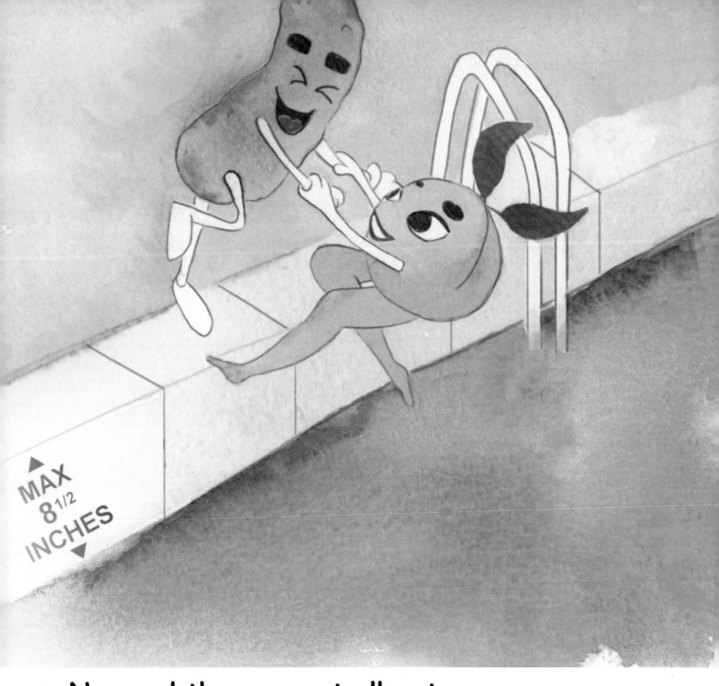

Now and then you get all wet...
and take that pickle deep!

He gyrates while you're whippin' eggs
and when you're packing fudge

He knows you like it different ways
...he's not one to judge

The nights that you are up 'til dawn
drinking with a friend

JiggleWiggleTicklePickle is happy to attend

When you and he, and she make three,
and everyone gets lucky

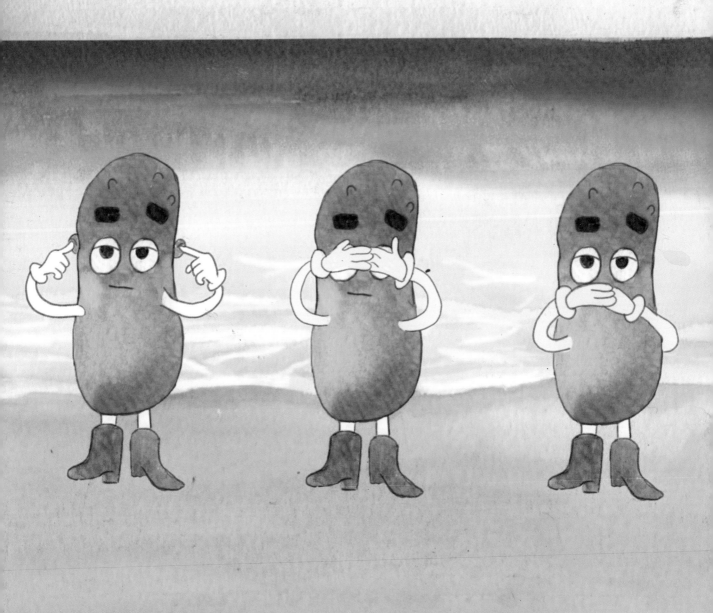

JiggleWiggleTicklePickle never tells his buddies

Each night as you turn out the light
    you reach for your nightstand

...'cause JiggleWiggleTicklePickle is the perfect man